DOWNTON A

ORIGINAL MUSIC FROM THE TELEVISION SERIES

WISE PUBLICATIONS
part of The Music Sales Group
London / New York / Paris / Sydney / Copenhagen / Berlin / Madrid / Hong Kong / Tokyo

Published by
Wise Publications
14-15 Berners Street, London W1T 3LJ, UK.

Exclusive Distributors:
Music Sales Limited
Distribution Centre, Newmarket Road,
Bury St Edmunds, Suffolk IP33 3YB, UK.
Music Sales Pty Limited
Units 3-4, 17 Willfox Street, Condell Park,
NSW 2200, Australia.

Order No. AM1006313
ISBN: 978-1-78305-022-2
This book © Copyright 2013 Wise Publications,
a division of Music Sales Limited.

Edited by Jenni Norey.
Arranged by Jeremy Birchall & Christopher Hussey.
Arrangements and engravings
supplied by Camden Music Services.

Printed in the EU.

Downton Abbey – The Suite

Music by John Lunn

8

9

10

Love And The Hunter

Music by John Lunn

18

Andante (♩ = 98)

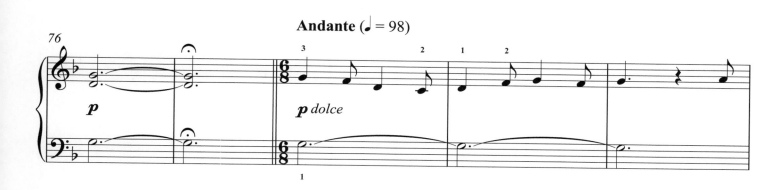

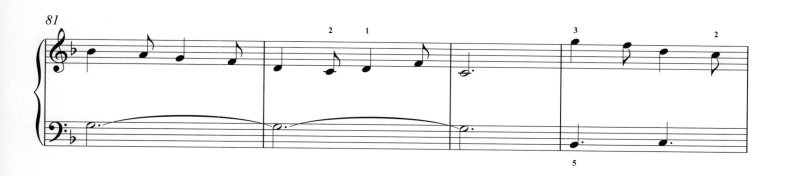

19

Emancipation

Music by John Lunn

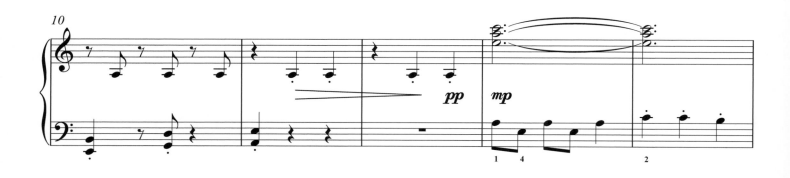

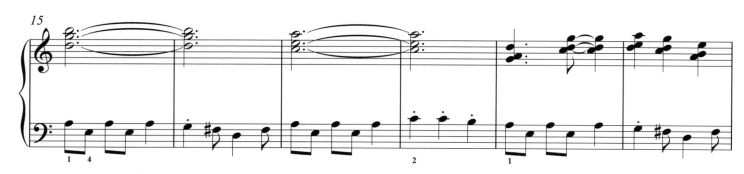

24

25

Story Of My Life

Music by John Lunn

Lento espressivo ♩ = 60

con Ped.

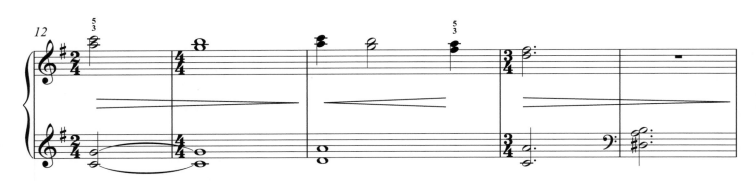

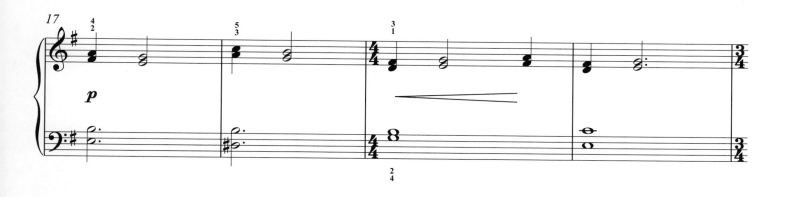

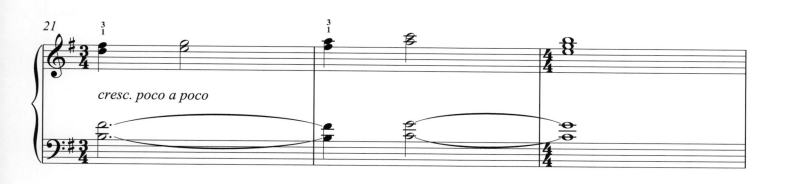

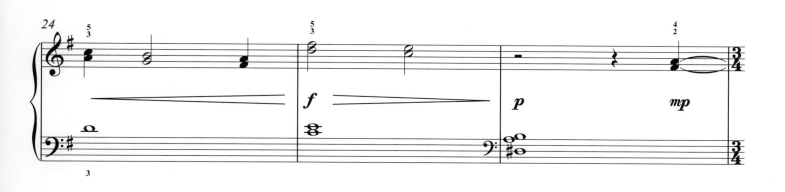

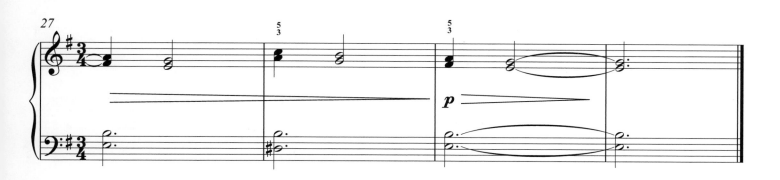

Fashion

Music by John Lunn

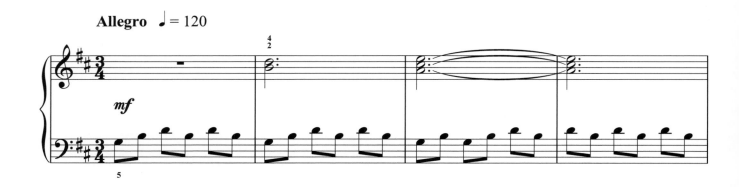

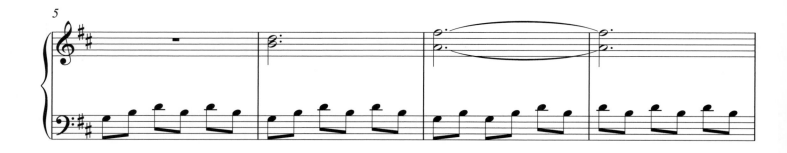

Damaged

Music by John Lunn

Adagio

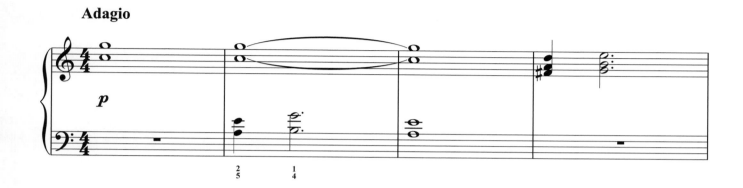

Andante

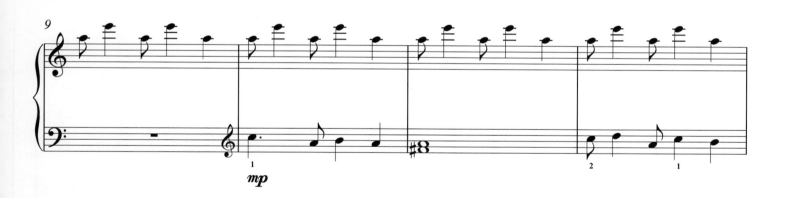

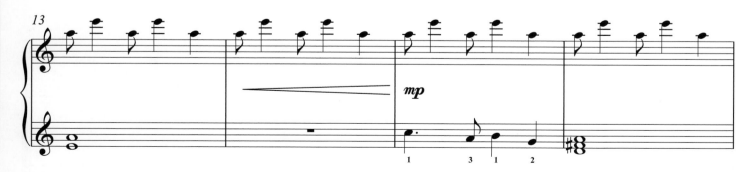

33

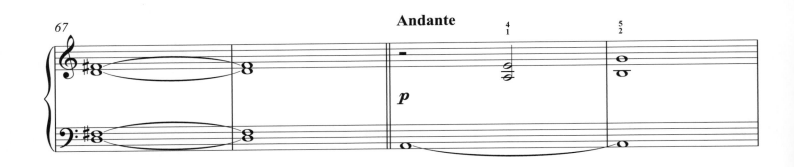

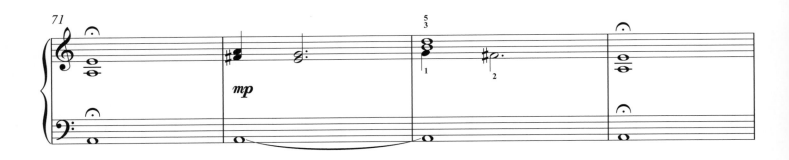

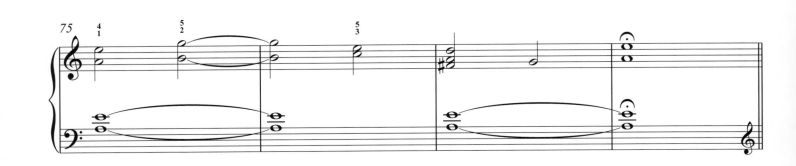

Preparation

Music by John Lunn

40

Us And Them

Music by John Lunn

44

Such Good Luck

Music by John Lunn

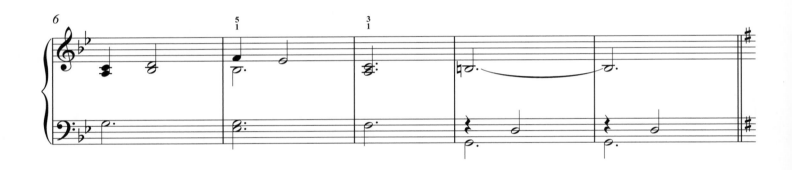

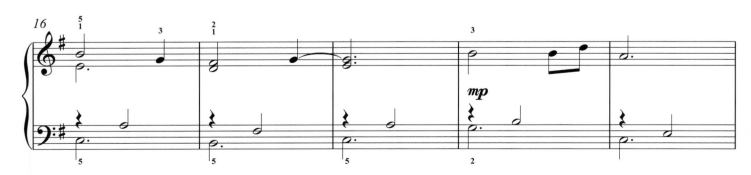

rit. poco a poco

Violet

Music by John Lunn

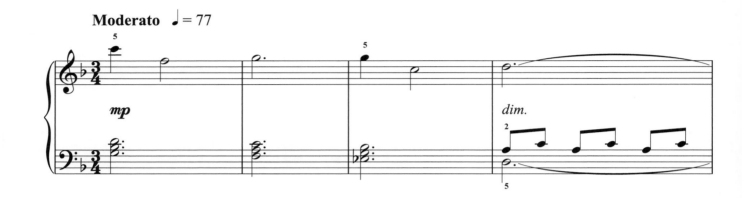

Meno mosso

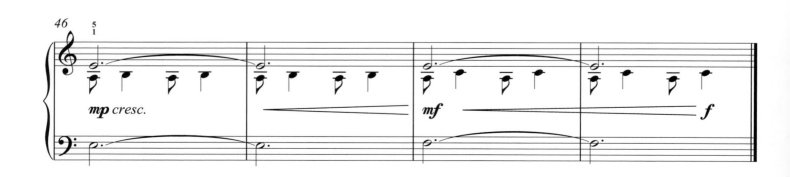

A Drive

Music by John Lunn

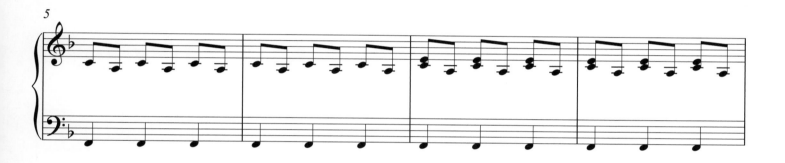

An Ideal Marriage

Music by John Lunn

Telegram

Music by John Lunn

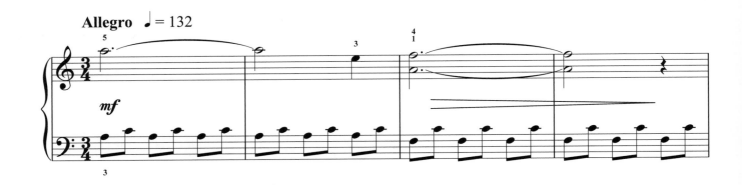

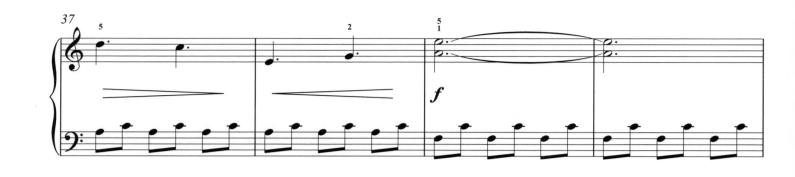

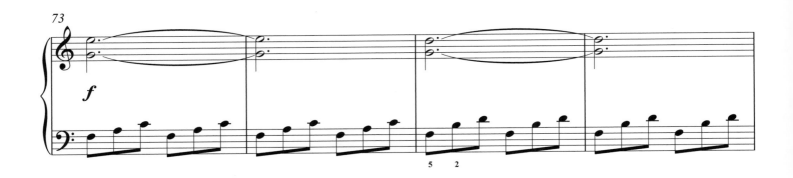

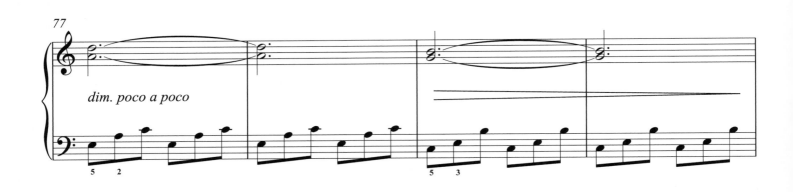

Deception

Music by John Lunn

Titanic

Music by John Lunn

Andante sostenuto ♩ = 96

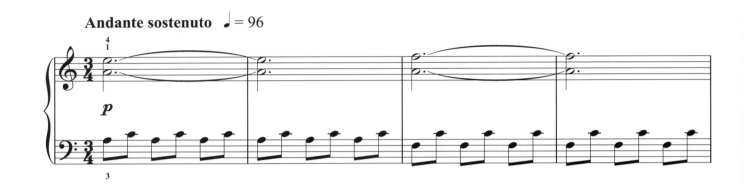

A Song And A Dance

Music by John Lunn

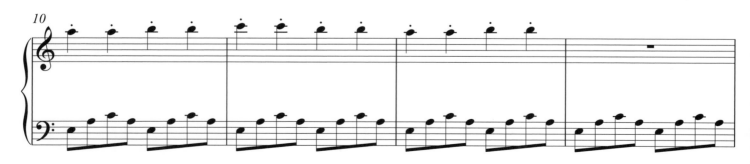

Did I Make The Most Of Loving You?

Music by John Lunn